FAIRY TALE FRACTURES

This hospital room is filled with nursery rhyme and fairy tale characters who are having a very tough day. Look for clues to tell you who each person is. Then try to figure out how they hurt themselves.

Answer on page 47.

FORECAST FUN

To let the sunshine through these clouds, forecast where these weather words will appear. Use the number of letters in each word as a clue to figure out where it fits in the boxes on the next page. It may help to cross each word off the list as you use it. Don't feel any pressure, because this should be a breeze.

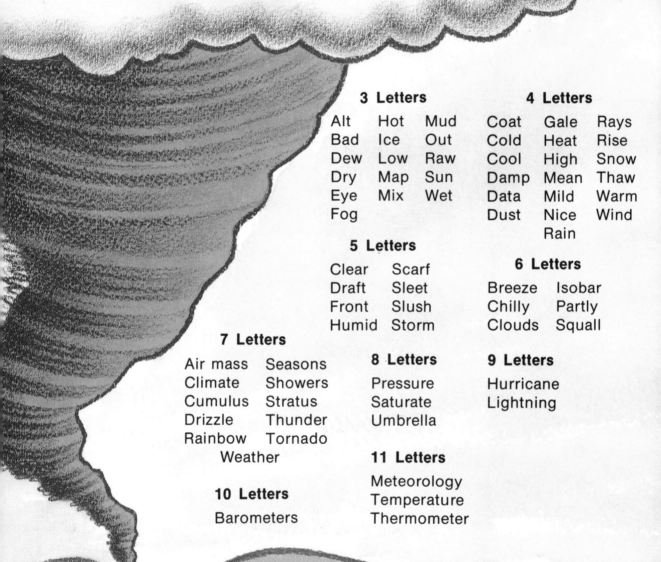

3 Letters

Alt	Hot	Mud
Bad	Ice	Out
Dew	Low	Raw
Dry	Map	Sun
Eye	Mix	Wet
Fog		

4 Letters

Coat	Gale	Rays
Cold	Heat	Rise
Cool	High	Snow
Damp	Mean	Thaw
Data	Mild	Warm
Dust	Nice	Wind
	Rain	

5 Letters

Clear	Scarf
Draft	Sleet
Front	Slush
Humid	Storm

6 Letters

Breeze	Isobar
Chilly	Partly
Clouds	Squall

7 Letters

Air mass	Seasons
Climate	Showers
Cumulus	Stratus
Drizzle	Thunder
Rainbow	Tornado
Weather	

8 Letters

Pressure
Saturate
Umbrella

9 Letters

Hurricane
Lightning

11 Letters

Meteorology
Temperature
Thermometer

10 Letters

Barometers

Illustrated by Richard Johnson

VOLLEY FOLLY

How many differences can you spot between these two pictures?

DOT MAGIC

Connect these dots if you'd like to find someplace where no one will bother you.

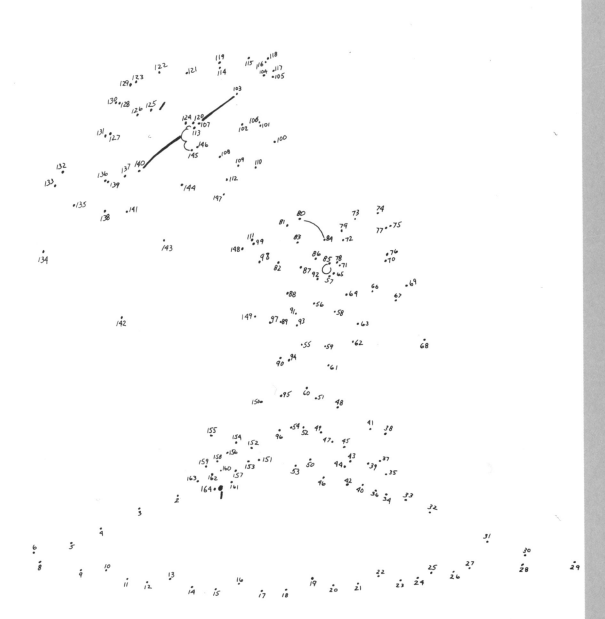

Illustrated by Rob Sepanak

AWKWARD ORCHARD

Rebus Rita spent her vacation on Uncle Jack's tree farm. As a gift for her uncle, she made up signs for the different kinds of trees. Can you figure out what trees Rita has pictured?

KEEP IT UNDER YOUR HAT

Freddy Fedora, the dry cleaner's son, thinks he's so funny. Using the hats in the shop, he left this code so his father would get a laugh. Look at the key below and then try to unravel his riddle.

Illustrated by R. Michael Palan

Answer on page 47.

ROW, ROW, ROW

Each of these Special Olympics competitors has something in common with the athletes in the same row. For example, all the athletes in the top row across are wearing red shorts. Look at the other rows across, down, and diagonally. What's the same about each row of three?

Illustrated by Anni Matsick

Answer on page 47.

MUMMY MAZE

Morton the Mummy has forgotten the secret passage to his royal chamber. Can you help him find his way back?

FINISH

Illustrated by Gregg Valley

GLOBE PROBE

That world famous adventurer, Cincinnati Holmes, drew a lot of pictures on his last trip. But the labels blew off each picture, and Cincinnati needs help remembering which country is pictured in each scene. Label each picture with the name of the country it represents, then locate each country on Cincy's world map.

4. _____

1. _____

2. _____

3. _____

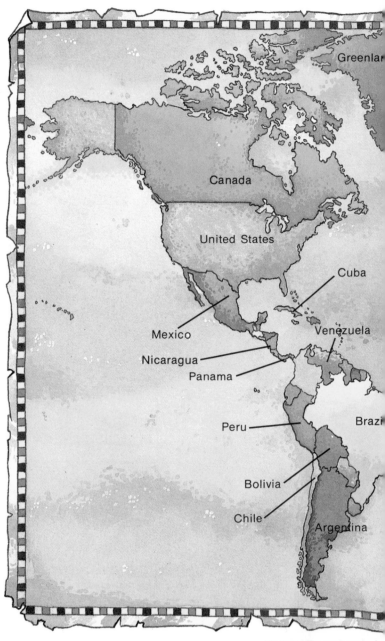

Illustrated by John Nez

5. _____

6. _____

7. _____

8. _____

L LIST

Under each category, list three things that begin with the letter L. For example, one flower that begins with L is Lamb's Ears. See if you can name three others.

FLOWERS

_____

_____

_____

BIG CATS

_____

_____

_____

CANDY

_____

_____

_____

U.S. CAPITALS

_____

_____

_____

Illustrated by Lisa Dayer

Answer on page 48.

FLAG FEATURE

Here's a chance to design some flags for your very own country. What colors and designs will you put in? What symbols are important to you? Use your imagination to draw in the flags that will tell the rest of the world about you.

Illustrated by Rob Sepanak

PLANT PUZZLE

This puzzle works just like a normal crossword, except instead of working up or down, you work clockwise or counterclockwise. Each clue matches a numbered petal. Start your answer at the number and work toward the center of the flower. Both of the first ones are done to get you started.

Clockwise

1. Dirt
2. Chatter
3. Prized red flower
4. Moist
5. A rake, hoe, or spade
6. Smallest amount of rain
7. Kernels on the cob
8. To bend out of shape by pressure or water
9. Weeding tools
10. Purple or red root vegetable
11. I will do it by my____
12. Cooperative group or players
13. Beef and pork
14. To loan
15. Winged animal
16. To stack in a wheelbarrow
17. Gardener's enemy
18. Lima, pinto, or string

Counterclockwise

1. Plant's beginning
2. Froglike creature
3. Precipitation
4. Toy baby
5. Job
6. Rounded building top
7. A field's yield
8. Sheep's hair
9. Stringed instrument
10. Birthed
11. To leak slowly
12. Holders for golf balls
13. What ice will do in the sun
14. Food-producing part of plant
15. A ray of sunlight
16. Bits of thread, etc.
17. What you write for each clue
18. Part of a necklace

Illustrated by Terry Rogers

SIMILAR SUITS

These suits of armor are on display in the Puzzlevania museum. They may all look similar, but only two match exactly. Can you find them?

Answer on page 48.

Illustrated by Jon Davis

20

AIRPORT MEMORIES

Take a long look at this picture. Try to remember everything you see in it. Then turn the page, and try to answer some questions about it without looking back.

Illustrated by Anni Matsick

DON'T READ THIS UNTIL YOU HAVE LOOKED AT "Airport Memories—Part 1" ON PAGE 21.

AIRPORT MEMORIES   Part 2

Can you answer these questions about the airport scene you saw? Don't peek!

1. What terminal was this?
2. What airline was the family flying?
3. Where was the family going?
4. What color was the father's shirt?
5. How many blue suitcases were on the conveyor belt?
6. What color was the plane just landing outside?
7. What did the girl have in her carrier?
8. What was around the father's neck?

Answer on page 48.

SIDE SIGHTS

Each picture below shows the side view of an ordinary clothing item.
Look closely and see if you can tell what each thing is.

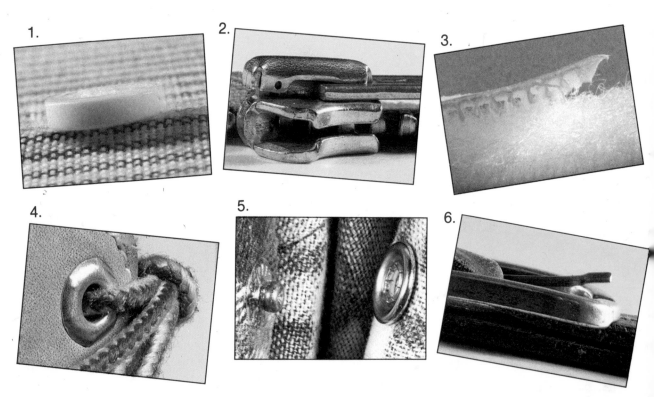

1.
2.
3.
4.
5.
6.

MORNING MESSAGE

A tableful of delicious breakfast foods are hidden in the letters below. Look up, down, across, backward, and diagonally to find them all. When you've digested the list, the leftover letters will give you a morning message.

BACON
BAGEL
BISCUITS
BRAN
BREAD
CEREAL
COFFEE
CREPE
EGGS
FRUIT

HAM
HONEY
JAMS
JELLY
JUICE
MILK
MUFFINS
OMELET
PANCAKES
SAUSAGE

STEAK
SUGAR
SYRUP
TART
TEA
TOAST
YOGURT

```
B A C O N M U F F I N S
I J S D E G A S U A S T
S T U L A E R E C T A E
C E R I R E T C S T H A
U L E A C D R A U Y T K
I E O F T E F B G S R L
T M C I P A N C A K E S
S O O E U G H O R G T H
K N F E R A T T A S A O
L A F G Y H O B M O D N
I R E M S A E A S G G E
M B E T A M J E L L Y Y
Y O G U R T T I U R F L
```

Leftover letters: _____

HIDDEN PICTURES

There are at least 20 objects hidden in this picture. How many can you find?

THE EMPEROR'S FEAST

The Emperor of Erminia is planning a feast for his visitors, Prince Peridot, King Kandu, Rajah Roger, and the Sultan of Sandar. There are nine different meats the cook can prepare: pheasant, pork roast, shrimp, glazed ham, roast beef, lobster, baked chicken, leg of lamb, and stuffed quail. The problem is:

The Sultan of Sandar never eats beef.

Prince Peridot does not like pheasant or the taste of glazed ham.

King Kandu is allergic to any kind of seafood.

The Rajah dislikes chicken.

What three meat dishes can the cook prepare which will please all the guests?

Answer on page 48.

9 BY 9

To complete this puzzle, put a single number from 1 to 9 into each of the empty boxes, in such a way that no number is repeated in any row, column, or even within the same square. For a real challenge, the numbers should not repeat in any row or column within the big square.

	2	5
4	3	—
—	—	8

—	—	4
—	5	2
3	7	—

8	3	—
—	1	—
5	—	2

5	4	—
—	9	—
2	—	3

—	2	8
5	—	3
9	—	—

—	9	—
—	2	8
7	—	6

6	7	—
8	—	9
—	—	4

4	—	—
—	3	6
2	8	—

3	—	1
—	—	4
9	6	—

PICTURE MIXER

Copy these mixed-up squares in the spaces on the next page to put this picture back together. The letters and numbers tell you where each square belongs. The first one, A-3, has been done for you.

A-3　A-2　A-1　A-4

B-1　B-3　B-4　B-2

C-2　C-3　C-1　C-4

D-1　D-4　D-2　D-3

Illustrated by Rob Sepanak

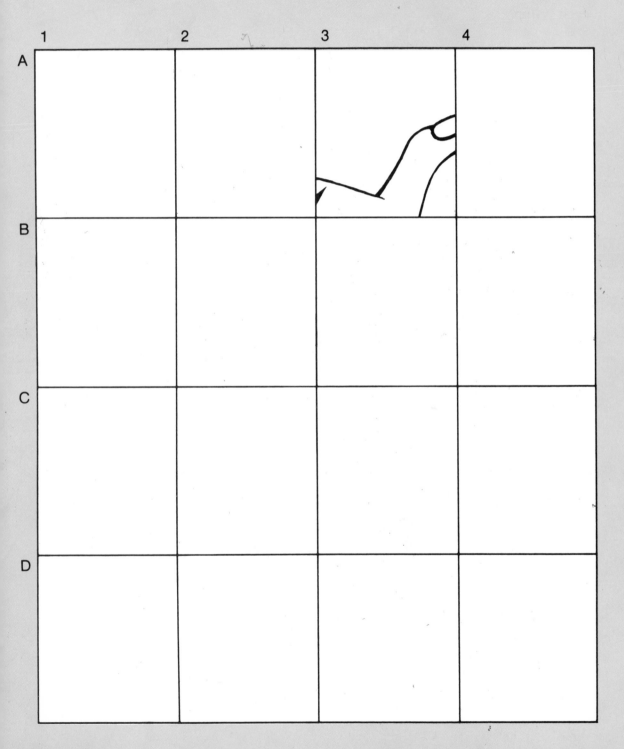

	1	2	3	4
A				
B				
C				
D				

SPORTS TALK

Each group of words is used in a specific sport. Can you play through and figure out what sport goes with each group?

Answer on page 48.

1. Set, Love, Fault, Deuce
2. Saber, Touché, Foil, En Garde
3. Field Goal, Downs, Pass, Interception
4. Dunk, Dribble, Jump ball, Free throw
5. Shutout, Diamond, Inning, Dugout
6. Silks, Handicap, Pulling, Steward
7. Stem Turn, Slalom, Snowplowing, Alpine
8. Broaching, Tacking, Yawing, Heaving To

Illustrated by Terry Rogers

ACE OF ACES

Each of these words ends with the letters "ACE." Use the clues to figure out the missing letters and fill in the words. If you can put all the right words in place, you'll be a puzzle-solving ace.

1. Your eyes, nose, and mouth help make this: ___ ace

2. To run in competition: ___ ace

3. Frilly material for trimming: ___ ace

4. Copy by drawing lightly over another picture: ___ ___ ace

5. Extra support, as on crooked teeth: ___ ___ ace

6. Where rocket ships blast off to: ___ ___ ace

7. Prayer said before some family meals: ___ ___ ace

8. Home for a king: ___ ___ ___ ace

9. The outside layer, or to come up from below the water: ___ ___ ___ ___ ace

10. Facial expression of pain or dislike: ___ ___ ___ ___ ace

11. To grasp lovingly: ___ ___ ___ ___ ace

12. Spot for a cozy blaze in the house: ___ ___ ___ ' ___ ___ ___ ace

Illustrated by Paul Richer

Answer on page 49.

THE MOUSE HOUSE

Put the words below into the spaces on the next page to finish the poem.

alone	cheese	home	place
appeared	face	house	please
before	floor	mouse	weird

Once I saw a pumpkin

That was bigger than a _____ .

1

Within, there lived a creature,

A giant, fuzzy _____ .

2

I walked into the pumpkin, feeling very _____ ,

3

Everything was in its proper _____ .

4

A door slid open, the creature _____

5

With a smile on his _____ .

6

"Will you have some tea?" he asked.

"Or perhaps a slice of _____ ?

7

How about a crumb of bread?

Oh, have some, won't you, _____ ?"

8

I learned his name was Murphy,

This pumpkin was his _____ .

9

He did not have many visitors,

Living here _____ .

10

I looked at Murphy, and with a grin,

I sat down on the _____ .

11

I happily ate with this fuzzy mouse

Since I'd never done so _____ .

12

Answer on page 49.

FIRST DAY

Today is Evelyn's first day at her new school. Can you number these pictures to show what happened first, second, and so on?

Answer on page 49.

WHAT'S IN A WORD?

There are lots of great activities in every issue of Puzzlemania. But there are also more than 70 terrific words in the letters of the word PUZZLEMANIA. PUZZLE and MAN are just two of them. How many words of three letters or more can you find hidden in PUZZLEMANIA?

ACE OF ACE

Each of these words e
clues to figure out th
you can put all the r
solving ace.

1. Your
2. To r
3. Fri
4. C
5. E
6.
7.

Illustrated

Answer on page 49.

THE WONDERFUL COLORING MACHINE

This mechanical marvel usually makes color coordination easy. All you do is put a colored shape into one side of the machine and tell it to either add or subtract a similar shape of a different color. The machine whistles, toots, and hums before producing a shape with the new color. But today the machine is on the fritz. It can't decide which is the right shape and color to spit out. Can you figure out which shape and color is the correct answer to each of the combinations?

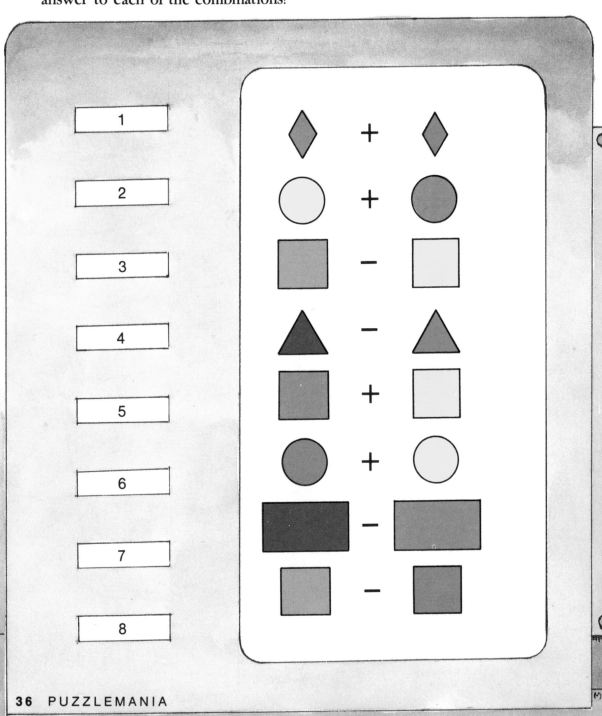

Answer on page 49.

MAP MISTAKES

How many mistakes can you find on this map?

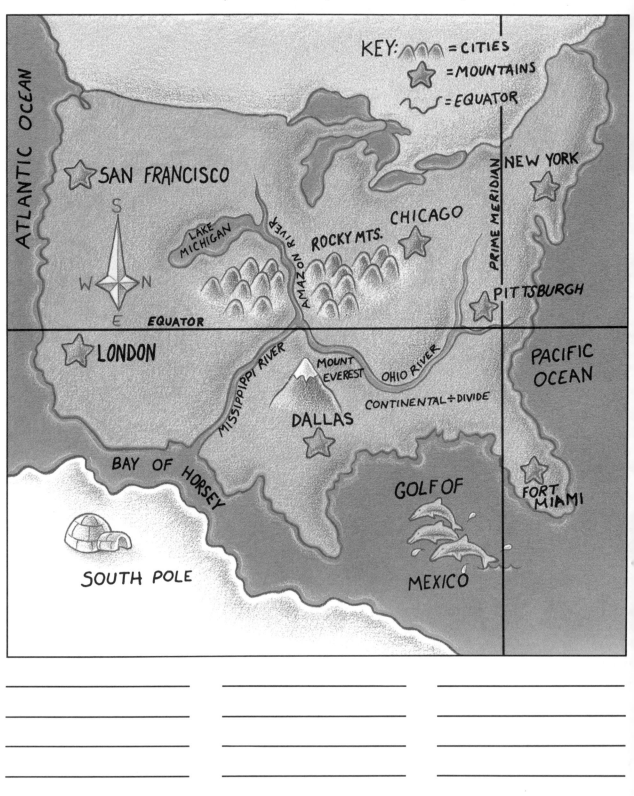

_____   _____   _____
_____   _____   _____
_____   _____   _____
_____   _____   _____
_____   _____   _____

Answer on page 49.

ALPHA-BIRDICAL

To complete the names of this flock of North American birds, fill in each blank with a different letter of the alphabet. Use the description to help identify each bird. Each letter of the alphabet will only be used once, so cross it off as you find a place for it to nest.

A B C D E F G H I J K L M N O P Q R S T U V W X Y Z

Answer on page 49.

1. __ ite	graceful, gliding, pointy-winged bird of prey
2. wa __ wi __ g	crested berry-eating beauty, Bohemian or Cedar
3. do __ e	peaceful branch-bearer
4. g __ l __	snowy swimmer and shoreline scavenger
5. ra __ orb __ ll	thick-beaked Atlantic auk
6. woo __ pe __ ke __	a wood-borer with a bill like a drill
7. __ a __	showy, noisy, bold blue bird
8. r __ __ in	red-breasted Springtime symbol
9. __ u __ il	grouse-like ground-dwelling gamebird
10. __ __ arro __	Song, Swamp, Field, and Chipping, for example
11. __ rackl __	blue-headed, boat-tailed blackbird
12. __ inc __	small, seed-eating, blunt-billed bird
13. __ ar __ in	"purple" swallow that loves apartment living

THE CASE OF THE GHOSTLY GROVE

See if you can solve this mystery. Read the story and fill in the missing words. Then match the numbered letters with the corresponding spaces at the end of the story. If you've filled in the spaces correctly, you'll find out what was haunting the forest.

Ralph Rabbit hopped as fast as his long hind __ __ __ __ could propel
                                                20 2
him. He was late again, and his mother would scold him for sure. The

__ __ __ had already set in the __ __ __ __ ; and it was getting dark, so
23   5

he took a shortcut through a large grove of tall oak __ __ __ __ __ . His
                                                        8

friends said the area was haunted, but Ralph didn't believe in __ __ __ __ __ __ .
                                                                  9

As he hopped down the narrow path, Ralph straightened his long

__ __ __ __ and listened to the familiar sounds. He heard the croak of a
 4

__ __ __ __ , the chirp of a baby __ __ __ __ , and the hoot of an
14   16 17

__ __ __ . But suddenly, halfway through the grove, he saw two glowing
 12

__ __ __ __ staring at him! He hurried on, and two more spooky eyes
        3

appeared among the fluttering __ __ __ __ __ __ of the trees. He looked
                                10   22

to the right, and there were eyes. He looked to the __ __ __ __ , and there
                                                      19

were more eyes! The entire grove seemed to be glaring at him. Poor Ralph's

__ __ __ __ __ pounded with fear.
 7   6

Ralph raced through the woods. With a last desperate leap, Ralph reached the

end of the path and landed on the doorstep of his own __ __ __ __ __ .
                                                        1 11

Even his fluffy tail was shaking with __ __ __ __ __ __ as he scrambled
                                        15   21

through the door.

"You're late again!" scolded his mother. Then, seeing him shiver, she said,

"Why, Ralph, whatever is the matter?"

"I've been chased by ghosts!" gasped Ralph, and he told both his

___ ___ ___ ___ ___ ___ ___ about the threatening eyes.
     18

"Nonsense!" said his father. "There are no ghosts in that grove. I'll go

check." And he went out the ___ ___ ___ ___ .
                     13

In a few minutes he returned, laughing. Papa Rabbit said, "It

wasn't ghosts you saw, Ralph!"

What was it that Ralph saw in the woods?   ___ ___   ___ ___ ___
                                         1 2   3 4 5

___ ___ ___   ___ ___ ___ ___   ___ ___   ___ ___ ___ ___ ___ ___ ___ ___ ___ .
6 7 8   9 10 11 12   13 14   15 16 17 18 19 20 21 22 23

Answer on page 49.

WHAT AM I?

Can you guess the answer before you reach the final clue?

1. I am an annual or biennial herb.

2. I am a member of the genus RAPHANUS, and a member of the mustard family CRUCIFERAE.

3. It is believed that I originated in China, but today I can be found throughout the North Temperate Zone.

4. I can vary in size and shape, and can be white or yellow, but usually I am red on the outside and white on the inside.

5. I grow very quickly; some varieties of me take only a month to grow from seed to harvest.

6. A large white version of me from Japan is called DAIKON.

7. I am often eaten raw in salads, but I can also be pickled or cooked.

8. My taste can vary from mild to hot.

What am I?

Answer on page 49.

▌NSTANT PICTURE

To discover something that will give you a bumpy ride, fill in
each section that contains only one dot.

Answer on page 50.

GRANNY'S GROCERIES

Great groups of things begin with the letters "GR." Grope
through these pages to see how many GR words you can find.
If you find more than 30, give yourself a grand grade.

DAFFY TAFFY

Toni, Timmy, and Tammy were stretching this fresh taffy when things got out of hand. To help get things under control, can you match each puller with a bowl to put the taffy in?

Answer on page 50.

ANSWERS

FAIRY TALE FRACTURES (page 3)
In the waiting room are:

The Big Bad Wolf, who huffed and puffed his cheeks out trying to bring down the pig's brick house

Sleeping Beauty, who stuck her finger on a sewing needle

Humpty Dumpty, who fell off his wall

Snow White, who ate a poisoned apple

Jack and Jill, who fell down the hill

Jack Be Nimble, who got burned jumping over his candlestick

FORECAST FUN (pages 4-5)

DOT MAGIC (page 7)

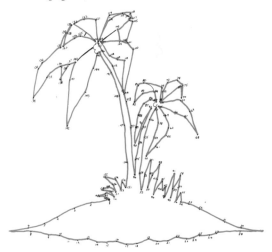

AWKWARD ORCHARD (pages 8-9)
1. cherry
2. teak
3. cedar
4. palm
5. pine
6. cypress
7. hemlock
8. beech
9. willow
10. walnut
11. maple

KEEP IT UNDER YOUR HAT (pages 10-11)
What did the necktie say to the hat?
"You go on ahead. I'll hang around here."

ROW, ROW, ROW (page 12)

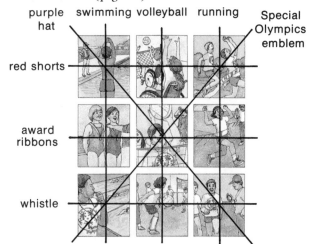

MUMMY MAZE (page 13)

GLOBE PROBE (pages 14-15)
The answer appears on page 50.

L LIST (page 16)
Here are the answers we found. You may have found some others.

Flowers	Big Cats
Lily	Lion
Lilac	Leopard
Larkspur	Lynx

Candy	U.S. Capitals
Lollipop	Lansing
Licorice	Little Rock
Lemon drops	Lincoln

PLANT PUZZLE (pages 18-19)

SIMILAR SUITS (page 20)

AIRPORT MEMORIES (page 22)
1. Terminal C
2. Flymore Airlines
3. Miami
4. Red
5. Two
6. Green
7. A dog
8. A camera

SIDE SIGHTS (page 22)
1. button
2. zipper
3. velcro
4. shoelace
5. snaps
6. belt

MORNING MESSAGE (page 23)

Start the day off right. Eat a good meal.

THE EMPEROR'S FEAST (page 26)
Pork roast, leg of lamb, and stuffed quail are the three meats everyone will eat.

9 BY 9 (page 27)

9 2 5	6 1 4	8 3 7
4 3 7	8 5 2	6 1 9
1 6 8	3 7 9	5 4 2
5 4 6	7 2 8	1 9 3
7 9 1	5 6 3	4 2 8
2 8 3	9 4 1	7 5 6
6 7 2	4 9 5	3 8 1
8 5 9	1 3 6	2 7 4
3 1 4	2 8 7	9 6 5

PICTURE MIXER (pages 28-29)

SPORTS TALK (page 30)
1. Tennis
2. Fencing
3. Football
4. Basketball
5. Baseball
6. Horse racing
7. Skiing
8. Sailing

ACE OF ACES (page 31)

1. face
2. race
3. lace
4. trace
5. brace
6. space
7. grace
8. palace
9. surface
10. grimace
11. embrace
12. fireplace

THE MOUSE HOUSE (pages 32-33)

1. House
2. Mouse
3. Weird
4. Place
5. Appeared
6. Face
7. Cheese
8. Please
9. Home
10. Alone
11. Floor
12. Before

FIRST DAY (page 34)

3 5
4 1
6 2

WHAT'S IN A WORD? (page 35)

Here are the words we found. You may have found others.

ail	lane	map	nip	pile
aim	lap	maple	nuzzle	pin
alm	lean	maul	pail	pine
alum	leap	maze	pain	pizza
amaze	lei	meal	pal	plain
amen	lie	mean	pale	plan
amp	lime	menial	palm	plane
animal	line	mile	pan	plaza
ape	lip	mine	pane	plea
elm	mail	mule	panel	plum
imp	main	muzzle	pea	pun
impale	maize	nail	peal	unzip
lain	male	name	pen	zap
lame	mane	nap	pie	zeal
lamp	manual	nape	pier	zip

THE WONDERFUL COLORING MACHINE (pages 36-37)

1. B
2. A
3. C
4. C
5. A
6. A
7. B
8. C

MAP MISTAKES (page 38)

The Amazon River is in South America.
London is in Europe.
The key is all wrong.
The compass markings are mixed up.
The Atlantic and Pacific are switched.
The equator does not run through the U.S.
The South Pole is much further south.
New York is further south.
Golf should be Gulf.
Miami is not a fort.
Mount Everest is in Asia.
The Mississippi River is misspelled.
The Mississippi is further east.
Lake Michigan is further north.
There is no Bay of Horsey.

Almost everything else is wrong on this map, too!
Any atlas will show you where the mistakes are.

ALPHA-BIRDICAL (page 39)

1. kite
2. waxwing
3. dove
4. gull
5. razorbill
6. woodpecker
7. jay
8. robin
9. quail
10. sparrow
11. grackle
12. finch
13. martin

THE CASE OF THE GHOSTLY GROVE (pages 40-41)

Ralph Rabbit hopped as fast as his long hind LEGS could propel him. He was late again, and his mother would scold him for sure. The SUN had already set in the WEST; and it was getting dark, so he took a shortcut through a large grove of tall oak TREES. His friends said the area was haunted, but Ralph didn't believe in GHOSTS.

As he hopped down the narrow path, Ralph straightened his long EARS and listened to the familiar sounds. He heard the croak of a FROG, the chirp of a baby BIRD, and the hoot of an OWL. But suddenly, halfway through the grove, he saw two glowing EYES staring at him! He hurried on, and two more spooky eyes appeared among the fluttering LEAVES of the trees. He looked to the right, and there were eyes. He looked to the LEFT, and there were more eyes! The entire grove seemed to be glaring at him. Poor Ralph's HEART pounded with fear.

Ralph raced through the woods. With a last desperate leap, Ralph reached the end of the path and landed on the doorstep of his own HOUSE. Even his fluffy tail was shaking with FRIGHT as he scrambled through the door.

"You're late again!" scolded his mother. Then, seeing him shiver, she said, "Why, Ralph, whatever is the matter?"

"I've been chased by ghosts!" gasped Ralph, and he told both his PARENTS about the threatening eyes.

"Nonsense!" said his father. "There are no ghosts in that grove. I'll go check." And he went out the DOOR.

In a few minutes he returned, laughing. Papa Rabbit said, "It wasn't ghosts you saw, Ralph!"
What was it that Ralph saw in the woods?

H E S A W T H E G L O W O F
1 2 3 4 5 6 7 8 9 10 11 12 13 14

F I R E F L I E S .
15 16 17 18 19 20 21 22 23

WHAT AM I? (page 42)
Radish

INSTANT PICTURE (page 43)

DAFFY TAFFY (page 46)

GLOBE PROBE (pages 14-15)

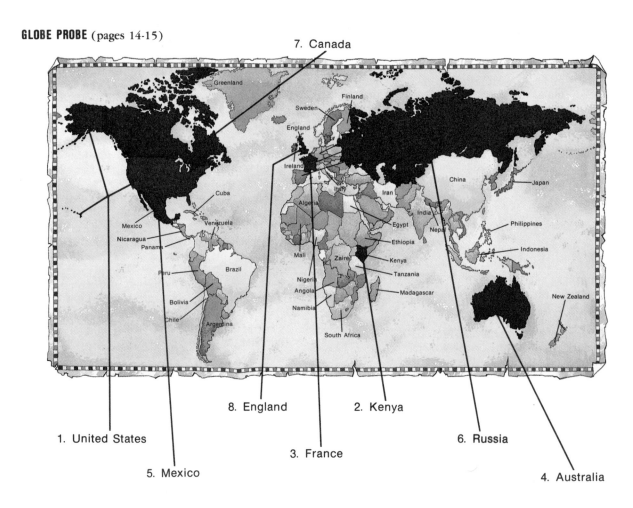

7. Canada

Greenland

Finland
Sweden
England

Ireland

China
Japan

Cuba

Italy
Iran

Algeria
India

Mexico
Egypt
Nepal
Philippines

Venezuela

Nicaragua
Ethiopia
Indonesia

Panama

Mali
Zaire
Kenya

Peru
Brazil
Tanzania

Nigeria
Madagascar

Bolivia
Angola

Chile
Namibia
New Zealand

Argentina

South Africa

8. England   2. Kenya

1. United States   6. Russia

3. France

5. Mexico   4. Australia